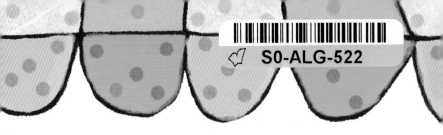

ABC 英文歌謠

40首經典英文歌謠，陪孩子快樂學習ABC

風車圖書
WINDMILL

目錄

"Good Morning"

Good morning!
Good morning! To you!
To you! And To you!
Good morning!
Good morning! To you
And to you! Peter, Dandy,
Paul and John, Mary,
Susan, you and you!
Good morning!
Good morning!
To you! And to you!

早安！早安！你早！你早！你早！早安！早安！你早！你早！
彼得、丹迪、保羅和約翰，瑪麗、蘇珊、你和你！早安！
早安！你早！你早！

〔第2首〕

Brush! Brush! Brush Your Teeth

刷牙歌

Brush! Brush! Brush your teeth. Brush your teeth! Oh, yes! Merrily, merrily, merrily, merrily. Brush your teeth! Oh, yes!

刷牙！刷牙！刷你的牙！刷你的牙！喔耶！快樂的，快樂的，快樂的，快樂的！刷你的牙！喔耶！

One, two, buckle my shoes. Three, four, shut the door. Five, six, seven, eight, nine, ten. Let's go play!

一、二綁鞋帶，三、四關上門，五、六、七、八、九、十，
我們一起去玩吧！

〔第4首〕

Goodbye to You

再見歌

"Goodbye to You"

Goodbye to you.

Goodbye to you.

Goodbye my dear

friends.

I will see

you again.

再見吧！再見吧！再見我親愛的朋友！我將會再見到你！

〔第5首〕

Cock a Doodle Doo

公雞咕咕叫

Cock-a-doodle-doo!
My dame has lost
her shoe. My
master's lost his
fiddling stick. And
doesn't know what
to do. And doesn't
know what to do.

15

公雞咕咕咕，女主人丟了她的鞋，男主人丟了他的琴弓，不知
道該怎麼辦？不知道該怎麼辦？

〔第6首〕

Pop Goes the Weasel

碰！黃鼠狼跳出來

Half a pound of two-penny rice. Half a pound of treacle. That's the way the money goes. Pop goes the weasel.

半磅二便士的米，半磅的糖蜜，錢就是這麼花的。碰！黃鼠狼跳出來！

Fingers Song

手指歌謠

Where is Thumbkin?

Where is Thumbkin?

Here I am, here I am.

How are you this

morning? Very well,

I thank you! Run away!

Run away!

(2)Pointer (3)Tall man

(4)Ring man (5)Pinkie

大拇指，你在哪裡？大拇指，你在哪裡？我在這，我在這兒。
今天早上，你好嗎？我很好，謝謝你！再見囉！再見囉！(2)
食指 (3) 中指 (4) 無名指 (5) 小拇指

Who's afraid of the big bad wolf? Big bad wolf, big bad wolf. Who's afraid of the big bad wolf? La, La, La, La, La...

21

誰怕大野狼？大野狼，大野狼。誰怕大野狼？啦啦啦啦啦 ……。

"The Happy Wander"

I love to go a wandering along the mountain track. And as I go, I love to swing. My knapsack on my back. Val-de-ri, val-de-ra, val-de-ra, val-de-ra, ha, ha, ha, ha, ha. Val-de-ri, val-de-ra. My knapsack on my back.

我喜歡順著山徑徘徊遊蕩，我喜歡邊走路邊搖晃，背著我的帆布袋。吧一的一哩，吧一的一啦，吧一的一啦，吧一的一啦，哈，哈，哈，哈，哈，吧一的一哩，吧一的一啦，我背上的帆布袋。

〔第10首〕

Baa Baa
Black Sheep

咩咩叫的黑羊

Baa, Baa, Black sheep, have you any wool. Yes sir, yes sir, three bags full. One for my master and one for my dame. But none for the little boy that cries in the lake.

咩！咩！黑羊，你有羊毛嗎？有的，有的，我有滿滿的三袋。一袋要給我的主人，一袋要給我的女主人，但就是沒有給在湖邊哭泣的小男孩。

〔第11首〕
Johnny Works with One Hammer

強尼用一隻鐵槌工作

Johnny works
with one hammer.
One hammer,
one hammer.
Johnny works
with one hammer.
Johnny works
with one.

27

強尼用一隻鐵槌工作,一隻鐵槌,一隻鐵槌。強尼用一隻鐵槌
工作,強尼用一隻鐵槌工作。

〔第12首〕

Round the Mulberry Bush

繞著桑樹玩遊戲

Here we go round the mulberry bush. The mulberry bush, the mulberry bush. Here we go round the mulberry bush. So early in the morning.

29

我們一起繞著桑樹，繞著桑樹玩遊戲，繞著桑樹玩遊戲。我們一起繞著桑樹，在這個早晨。

〔第13首〕

Four Little Ducks

四隻小鴨

"Four Little Ducks"

Four little ducks went out one day. Over the hills and far away. Mother duck said: quack, quack, quack, quack. But only three little ducks came back.

有一天四隻小鴨外出，越過山丘，走了很遠、很遠。鴨媽媽呱呱呱呱的叫著，但只有三隻小鴨回來而已。

〔第14首〕

How Much is that Doggie?

那隻小狗狗多少錢？

How much is that doggie in the window?
The one with the waggily tail.
How much is that doggie in the window?
I do hope that doggie is for sale.

櫥窗裡小狗要多少錢呢？其中有一隻對我搖尾巴。櫥窗裡小狗要多少錢呢？我多希望那隻小狗狗是要出售的。

〔第15首〕

Lightly Row

輕輕划

"Lightly Row"

Lightly row, lightly row. O'er the glassy waves we'll go! Smoothly glide, smoothly glide on the silent tide! Let the wind and water be, mingled with the melody! Sing and float! Sing and float! In our little boat!

35

輕輕的划，輕輕的划，讓我們滑過光滑如鏡的水面！平穩的划動著，平穩的划動在平穩的潮水上，讓微風和潮水調和成美妙的樂章！邊唱邊漂流，邊唱邊漂流。在我們的小船上！

〔第16首〕

Two Little Eyes

兩隻小眼睛

"Two Little Eyes"

Two little eyes that open and close. Two little ears and one little nose. Two little cheeks and one little chin. Two little lips with the teeth close in.

兩隻小眼睛，張開來，閉起來，兩個小耳朵和一個小鼻子，兩個小臉頰和一個小下巴，兩片小嘴唇將牙齒關起來。

〔第17首〕

ABC's Song

字母歌

"ABC's Song"

A,B,C,D,E,F,G,H,I,J,
K,L,M,N,O,P,Q,R,S
AND T,U,V,W
AND X,Y,Z.
Happy, happy
shall we be,
When we learned
our A,B,C.

A,B,C,D,E,F,G,H,I,J,K,L,M,N,O,P,Q,R,S和T,U,V,W和X,Y,Z.
快樂，快樂將要來到，當我們學會我們的A,B,C。

〔第18首〕

Are You Sleeping?

你睡覺了嗎？

Are you sleeping?
Are you sleeping?
Brother John,
Brother John.
Wedding bells
are ringing.
Wedding bells
are ringing.
Ding ding-dong.
Ding ding-dong.

你睡著了嗎？你睡著了嗎？約翰兄弟，約翰兄弟。婚禮鐘聲響著，婚禮鐘聲響著。叮叮噹！叮叮噹！

〔第19首〕

Happy Birthday

生日快樂

"Happy Birthday"

Happy birthday
to you.
Happy birthday
to you.
Happy birthday
my dear friend.
Happy birthday
to you.

43

祝你生日快樂，祝你生日快樂，祝你生日快樂，我親愛的好朋友。祝你生日快樂。

〔第20首〕

I Saw
Three Ships

我看見三艘船

I saw three ships come sailing by, sailing by, sailing by. I saw three ships come sailing by, on Xmas day in the morning.

45

我看見了三艘船航行過，航行過，航行過。我看見了三艘船航行過，在耶誕節這天的清晨。

〔第21首〕

Jack in the Box

傑克在箱子裡

"Jack in the Box"

Jack in the box,
as quiet as a
mouse. Way down
inside, his dark
little house.
There he lies,
ever so still. Will
he come out?
Yes, he will!

傑克在箱子裡，安靜的像隻小老鼠。待在他那昏暗的小屋子裡
面。他一直就這樣靜靜待在那裡。傑克，他會出來嗎？是的，
他當然會！

〔第22首〕

The Wheels on the Bus

巴士的輪子

The wheels on
the bus go round
and round, round
and round, round
and round.
The wheels on
the bus go round
and round,
all day long.

巴士的輪子轉呀轉，轉呀轉，轉呀轉。巴士的輪子轉呀轉，轉
整天。

〔第23首〕

Fly Bird Fly

飛吧！飛吧！小小鳥

"Fly Bird Fly"

Fly, birdie, fly!

Fly, birdie, fly!

Fly, birdie, fly!

Up up to the sky!

La,La...La,La...

飛吧！飛吧！小小鳥！ 飛吧！飛吧！小小鳥！飛吧！飛吧！
小小鳥！ 飛上高高的天空！啦啦~啦啦~

Five Little Frogs

五隻小青蛙

Five little frogs
sitting on a well.
One leaned over
and down he fell.
Frogs leap high and
frogs leap low.
Now only four frogs
sitting in a row.

五隻小青蛙，坐在井邊，一隻身體一傾斜，就不小心掉到井裡
了！其他的青蛙急得上、下跳，現在只剩下四隻青蛙排排坐。

〔第25首〕

London Bridge

倫敦鐵橋垮下來

London Bridge is falling down, falling down, falling down. London Bridge is falling down, my fair lady. Build it up with iron bars, iron bars, iron bars. Build it up with iron bars, my fair lady.

倫敦鐵橋垮下來，垮下來，垮下來。倫敦鐵橋垮下來，我美麗
的姑娘！造橋要用鐵鋼條，鐵鋼條，鐵鋼條。造橋要用鐵鋼條
啊！我美麗的姑娘！

〔第26首〕

One, Two, Three, Four, Five

一、二、三、四、五

One, two, three, four, five, once I caught a fish alive. Six, seven, eight, nine, ten, then I let him go again. Why did you let him go? Because he bit my finger so. Which finger did he bite? This little finger on my right.

一、二、三、四、五，有一次我捉了一條活魚。六、七、八、九、十，然後我又再把牠放掉。為什麼你要放牠走呢？因為牠咬了我的手指頭啊！牠是咬到那隻手指頭呢？就是我右手的小指頭。

〔第27首〕

Did You Ever See a Lassie?

你曾看見一位少女嗎？

"Did You Ever See a Lassie?"

Did you ever see a lassie, a lassie, a lassie? Did you ever see a lassie, go this way and that? Go this way and that way, and this way, and that way. Did you ever see a lassie go this way and that?

59

你可曾看到一位少女，一位少女，一位少女？你可曾看到一位少女，從這邊和那邊走過？從這邊和那邊，這邊和那邊。你可曾看到一位少女，從這邊和那邊走過？

〔第28首〕

Rain Rain Go Away

雨呀雨呀快離開

"Rain Rain Go Away"

Rain, rain, go away. Come again another day. Little Johnny wants to play. Rain, rain, go to Spain. Never show your face again. Little Johnny wants to play. Rain on the green grass. Rain on the tree. Rain on the housetop. But not on me.

雨呀！雨呀！快離開！改天再來吧！小強尼想出去玩。雨呀！雨呀！去西班牙吧！別再露出你的臉，小強尼想出去玩。雨呀下在草地上，雨呀下在大樹上，雨呀下在屋頂上，但是，別打在我身上。

Do Re Mi

真善美

"Do Re Mi"

Do, a deer a female deer. Re, a drop of golden sun. Mi, a name I call myself. Fa, a long long way to run. So, a needle pulling thread. La, a note to follow So. Ti, a drink with jam and bread. That will bring us back to Do-oh-oh-oh! Do, Re, Me, Fa, So, La, Ti, Do, So, Do !

ㄅㄡ，一隻小鹿，一隻小母鹿，ㄖㄨㄟ，一道金色陽光，ㄇㄧ，一個我自稱的名字，ㄈㄚ，一條長長的路途，ㄙㄛ，一根針拉著線，ㄌㄚ，是ㄙㄛ後的一個音，ㄒㄧ，是一種和果醬、麵包一起用的飲料，那會把我們帶回ㄅㄡ，喔！喔！喔！ㄅㄡ、ㄖㄨㄟ、ㄇㄧ、ㄈㄚ、ㄙㄛ、ㄌㄚ、ㄒㄧ、ㄅㄡ、ㄙㄛ、ㄅㄡ！

On top of spaghetti,
all covered with
cheese. I lost my poor
meatball when
somebody sneezed.
It rolled off the table,
and onto the floor.
And then my poor
meatball rolled out
of the door.

在通心粉上，蓋滿了起司。我可憐的肉球沒了，因為有人打了一個大噴嚏。它滾出了桌子外頭，又滾到了地上，然後，我可憐的肉球就滾出了門外。

〔第31首〕

It's a Small World

小小世界

It's a small world after all.
It's a small world after all.
It's a small world after all.
It's a small, small world.
It's a world of laughter,
a world of tears. It's a
world of hope, and a world
of fears. There's so much
that we share. That it's time
we're aware. It's a small
world after all. It's a small
world after all. It's a small
world after all. It's a small
world after all. It's a small,
small world.

67

這是一個小小世界，這是一個小小世界，這是一個小小世界，
這是一個小小，小小世界。這個充滿了歡笑、眼淚、希望和恐
懼的世界，有那麼多我們要分享的。我們都須知道，這是一個
小小世界，這是一個小小世界，這是一個小小世界，這是一個
小小世界，這是一個小小，小小世界。

〔第32首〕

Hello

哈囉

"Hello"

Hello, hello. Hello, how are you?

I'm fine, I'm fine.

I hope that you are, too.

哈囉，哈囉，哈囉，哈囉，你好嗎？我很好。我很好。希望你也好。

〔第33首〕

Let's Sing Together

一起來唱歌

"Let's Sing Together"

Sing, sing together, merrily, merrily sing. Sing, sing together, merrily, merrily sing. Sing, sing, sing, sing.

唱歌，讓我們一起來唱歌。高高興興的，高高興興的唱歌。唱歌，讓我們一起來唱歌。高高興興，高高興興的唱歌。唱歌，唱歌，唱歌，唱歌。

〔第34首〕

Days of the week

一個星期

Sunday la-la-la,
Monday la-la-la,
Tuesday la-la-la,
Wednesday.
Thursday la-la-la,
Friday la-la-la,
Saturday. That
makes a week.

星期日，ㄌㄚ、ㄌㄚ、ㄌㄚ。星期一，ㄌㄚ、ㄌㄚ、ㄌㄚ。星期二，ㄌㄚ、ㄌㄚ、ㄌㄚ。星期三，星期四，ㄌㄚ、ㄌㄚ、ㄌㄚ。星期五，ㄌㄚ、ㄌㄚ、ㄌㄚ。星期六，這就是一個星期。

〔第35首〕

Twelve
Months

十二個月

"Twelve Months"

January, February,
March, April,
May and June,
July and August,
September,
October,
November,
December.

一月，二月，三月，四月，五月和六月，七月和八月，九月，
十月，十一月，十二月。

〔第36首〕

Row, Row, Row Your Boat

划呀划著你的船

Row, row, row
your boat.
Gently down
the stream.
Merrily, merrily,
merrily, merrily.
Life is but
a dream.

划呀，划著你的船。緩緩的順流而下。快樂的，歡欣的，快樂
的，歡欣的，人生就像一場夢。

〔第37首〕

The More We Get Together

當我們同在一起

"The More We Get Together"

The more we get together, together, together. The more we get together, the happier we'll be. For your friends are my friends. And my friends are your friends. The more we get together, the happier we'll be.

當我們同在一起，在一起，在一起。當我們同在一起，其快樂無比。你的朋友就是我的朋友。我的朋友就是你的朋友。當我們同在一起，其快樂無比。

Mary had a
little lamb,
little lamb,
little lamb.
Mary had a
little lamb.
Its fleece was
white as snow.

81

瑪麗有隻小綿羊。小綿羊，小綿羊。瑪麗有隻小綿羊。羊兒的
毛像雪那麼白。

Twinkle, twinkle, little star. How I wonder what you are! Up above the world so high. Like a diamond in the sky. Twinkle, twinkle, little star. How I wonder what you are!

83

一閃，一閃，小星星，美麗的小星星，高高掛在天空裡，像鑽石般的閃亮。一閃，一閃，小星星，美麗的小星星。

〔第40首〕

Polly, Put the Kettle on

寶莉，放上水壺

Polly, put the kettle on. Polly, put the kettle on. Polly, put the kettle on. We'll all have tea. Sukey, take it off again. Sukey, take it off again. Sukey, take it off again. They've all gone away.

寶莉，放上水壺。寶莉，放上水壺。寶莉，放上水壺。大家一起來喝茶。蘇姬，拿走水壺。蘇姬，拿走水壺。蘇姬，拿走水壺。大家都要離開了。

ABC英文歌謠 = ABC English songs ／ 常祈天,
蕭涵珍 編輯. -- 初版 -- 臺北市：風車圖書,
　　　　　2007. 08　面；　公分
ISBN　978-986-6855-35-1（精裝附光碟片）
　　1. 英語教學　2. 兒童歌謠
523.38　　　　　　　　　　　96013978

ABC英文歌謠

- 社長／許丁龍
- 編輯／常祈天、蕭涵珍
- 設計／邱月貞、蔡依雯
- 出版社／風車圖書出版有限公司
- 總代理／三暉圖書發行有限公司
- 地址／114台北市內湖區瑞光路258巷2號5樓
- 電話／02-8751-3866
- 傳真／02-8751-3858
- 網址／www.windmill.com.tw
- 劃撥／14957898
- 戶名／三暉圖書發行有限公司
- 初版／2007年08月